I Can See Them!

by Smriti Prasadam-Halls
Illustrated by Malgosia Piatkowska

OXFORD

UNIVERSITY PRESS

Anika stuffed her toy bunny into her rucksack and grabbed her coat from the hook. She was going to visit her cousins and didn't want to be <u>late</u>. She hadn't seen them in weeks.

   She was all packed and ready to go.

   Dad put on his new hat.

Anika is worried about being <u>late</u>. Have you ever been <u>late</u> for something? What happened?

The hat was bright green.
Anika got her bright red coat.

Anika tugged on her dad's arm. "Hurry up, Dad!" she said.

"I need to find my blue glasses first," replied Dad. He looked around.

"Is this <u>real</u> or are you joking again?" asked Anika. Her dad often played tricks on her.

"It's not a joke," Dad said. "I need my glasses."

Anika thinks her dad's story might not be <u>real</u>. Why does she think this?

"I might have left them by the kettle," said Dad.

Anika followed Dad into the kitchen. They <u>checked</u> by the kettle, on the table, and in the cupboard.

"There's something sticking out on the top shelf," said Anika.

Dad walked over. "Is it my glasses?" he asked.

Anika and her dad <u>check</u> by the kettle, on the table, and in the cupboard for the glasses. Can you think of anywhere else in the kitchen they might <u>check</u>?

It was not the glasses. It was a mug.

"I <u>probably</u> left them by the TV," said Dad.

"Come on, Dad!" cried Anika. "We are in a rush!"

Anika and Dad hurried into the living room. They looked by the TV and on the bookshelf.

"Can you see my glasses?" asked Dad.

Dad thinks he <u>probably</u> left his glasses by the TV. Does this mean he *did* leave them there, or he *might have* left them there?

It was not the glasses. It was a sock.

"I probably left them in the bathroom," said Dad.

"Hurry up, Dad!" moaned Anika. "We must go!"

They rushed into the bathroom. They looked by the sink and in the bath tub.

"Where are my glasses?" Dad asked. "Can you see them?"

It was not the glasses. It was a toothbrush.

Anika and Dad <u>searched</u> the whole house. They looked in the fridge, under the bed, in the oven, on top of the cupboard, and even in the dustbin! Dad's glasses were nowhere to be found.

Anika and Dad <u>searched</u> the whole house. Have you ever had to <u>search</u> for something?

Anika was sad.
Dad felt bad.

We cannot go on
the train trip.

Dad took off his new hat and scratched his head. "Wherever could my glasses be?"

"I can see them!" Anika yelled.

They were on top of Dad's head all along!

Dad and Anika rushed out of the house. They <u>arrived</u> at the train station just in time.

Dad and Anika <u>arrived</u> at the station just in time. Is there somewhere you have to <u>arrive</u> on time?

Retell the story

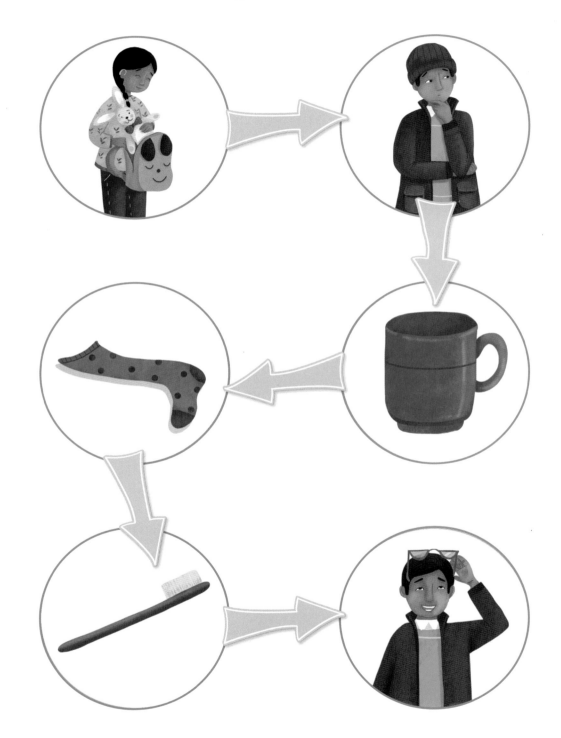